# Happy Ve...
## Book Th...

# Growing up

FRED J. SCHONELL

Illustrated by Eric Wade
and Kiddell-Monroe

**OLIVER AND BOYD: EDINBURGH**

### Note on the Revised Edition

HAPPY VENTURE was conceived and has been validated as a basic teaching method, and as such has proved outstandingly successful. Our language is a living one, however, and so certain expressions appearing in the original edition have now gone out of use.

Before his death in 1969, Professor Schonell was actively engaged in discussion with the publishers about the revision of the entire series. Unfortunately he was not able to undertake this before he died.

After consultations with practising teachers throughout the country and abroad, it became apparent to the publishers that the principles on which the series was based had not altered, but that minor changes to up-date the text could be made without affecting the well-tested structure of the series.

Accordingly, in this book, teachers will find:

> new illustrations except for animal stories; text up-dated, e.g. alterations to a 'pound' of butter on p. 38, steam engines on p. 39, and 'At the Fire Station' on p. 80; two nature stories substituted for 'The Lost Shoe' on pp. 59ff; consequent changes to Word List.

OLIVER & BOYD
Tweeddale Court
14 High Street
Edinburgh EH1 1YL
(A Division of Longman Group Limited)

*First Published* 1939
*Second Edition* 1959
*Revised Edition* 1971

ISBN 0 05 002381 0

© 1971 the Executors of the late
Sir Fred J. Schonell

Printed in Great Britain by
Robert Cunningham & Sons Ltd, Alva

# Contents

## Going to School

Dick will get his bag.
Dora will get her bag too.

Dick has his bag.
Dora has her bag too.
Dick and Dora are going
to school.

" Good-bye, Mummy," said Dick.
" Good-bye, Mummy," said Dora.

1

On the way to school
they met Jack and Jess.

Jack and Jess are going
to school. Jack has a kite.
He will let Dick play with it.

Jess has a doll.
She takes her doll to school.
She will let Dora play with it.

On the way to school
the children stop at a shop.

They look at the toys
in the shop.

Dick and Jack
look at a kite.

Then they all
run to school.

They go into school
and sit down.

Dick and Jack, Dora and Jess
are in school. See them
in the seats.

Dick has a book.
Jack has a book.
Dick's book is like Jack's book.

Jack reads his book.
Dick reads his book.

They read a funny story.
Dick reads a funny story
   to Jack.
Jack reads a funny story
   to Dick.

Dick reads well.
Jack reads well.

"I like a funny story,"
   said Jack.

Jess and Dora each have
   a book.

"I can read this story,"
   said Dora. "It is like the one
   in Dick's book."

"Yes," said Jess, "I can read
   the first story in the book.
   It is 'The Three Little Pigs.'"

Dora said, "I shall read
'The Three Little Pigs' to you."

## The Three Little Pigs

One day a mother pig said
  to her three little pigs,
" Now you are big, so big
  that you cannot all get
  in my house.
  You must each make a house.

But you must not
  let the big wolf catch you,"
  said Mother Pig.

" Oh no, he will not catch us,"
  said the three little pigs.

So each little pig went off
  to make a house.

The first little pig went
  down the road.  He met a man
  with some straw.

The little pig said to him,
" Please man, give me
    some straw."

" What do you want straw for ? "
    said the man.

" I want to make a house,"
    said the little pig.

"Then," said the man,
"you may have some straw."

So the first little pig took
the straw the man gave him,
and made a house of straw.

The second little pig went
down the road.  He met a man
with some sticks.

Second little pig said to him,
"Please man, will you give me
some sticks?"

"What do you want sticks for?"
said the man.

"I want to make a house,"
said the second little pig.

"Then," said the man,
"you may have some sticks."

7

So he gave some of the sticks
to the second little pig.

Second little pig went away
and made a house of sticks.

The third little pig went
down the road. He met a man
with some bricks.

"Please man, will you give me
some of your bricks?"

"What do you want bricks for?"
said the man.

"I want to make a house,"
said the third little pig.

"Then," said the man,
"you may have some bricks."

The man gave him some bricks.

The third little pig went away
and made a house of bricks.

Up came the wolf
to the first
pig's house
made of straw.

He tapped on the door.

"Little pig, little pig, let me in,"
he said.

Little pig said, "No, no.
By the hair of my chinny,
chin, chin,
I will not let you come in."

The wolf cried,
" Then I'll huff, and I'll puff,
and I'll blow your house in."

So he huffed, and he puffed,
and he blew the house in,
and ate up the little pig.

Then up went the wolf
to the house of sticks.

He tapped on the door.

" Little pig, little pig, let me in,"
he said.

Second little pig said, " No, no.
By the hair of my chinny,
chin, chin,
I will not let you come in."

" Then I'll huff, and I'll puff,
and I'll blow your house in,"
cried the wolf.

So he huffed, and he puffed,
and he blew the house in.
He ate up the second pig.

Then wolf went to the house
made of bricks, and said,
"Little pig, little pig, let me in.'

"No, no," said third little pig.
" By the hair of my chinny,
chin, chin,
I will not let you come in."

" Then I'll huff, and I'll puff,
and I'll blow your house in,"
cried the wolf.

So he huffed, and he puffed,
and he huffed, and he puffed,
but he could not blow down
the house made of bricks.

Then the wolf said, "Little pig,
little pig, will you come
in the morning at six o'clock
to get some turnips?"

"Yes," said the little pig.

In the morning at six o'clock
wolf tapped on the pig's door
and said,
"Are you ready, little pig?"

"Oh no," said the pig,
"I went to get my turnips
at five o'clock."

Then wolf said, "If you come
at five o'clock in the morning,
I'll take you
to an apple tree."

At four o'clock in the morning
pig went to get some apples.

He was in the apple tree
   when he saw the wolf
   coming up the road.

" Good morning, wolf,"
   he cried.
   " Look out,
   I'll throw you
   an apple."

Down the road
   went the apple,
   and the wolf
   ran to get it.

Then out of the tree
jumped the pig,
and ran fast to his house.

The wolf went to the house.
" Will you come to the fair
in the town ? " he said.

" Yes," said the little pig,
" I'll come at three o'clock."

But at two o'clock
little pig went to the fair.

And he was going home
with some apples and turnips,
when he saw the wolf
coming up the hill.

"What will I do ? " cried the pig.

He saw a barrel on the road.

He got into the barrel
and down the hill he went.

The wolf saw
the barrel
coming down
the hill.

"Oh, oh, oh!" he cried.
"What is this?
What is this?"

And home he ran,
as fast as he could go.

15

In the morning the wolf went
to the little pig's house.

He tapped on the door.

" Did you go to the fair
in the town ? " he said.

" Yes," said the pig, " I went,
but I did not see you."

" No," said the wolf,
" I was going up the hill
when I saw a big barrel
coming down the hill.
It was coming on top of me,
so I ran home
as fast as I could go."

" I was in that barrel,"
said the pig, " coming home
from the fair."

This made the wolf cry out.

" I will come down the chimney
and eat you," he said.

But the little pig had a pot
of hot water. The wolf
came down the chimney.
He fell into the pot,
and the pig put on the lid.

# Dinner Time

Dora and Dick have come home
from school.

Mummy said, " Please Dora,
will you set the table
for dinner ?  Dick, please
get some water for Nip."

Dora set the table.

Dick got some water for Nip.

"Bow-wow ! Bow-wow ! " said Nip.

" Oh, that must be Daddy,"
cried Dora.

" Daddy is home," cried Dick.

" I must wash," said Daddy,
" and then I will be ready
for dinner.

18

Now dinner is ready.

Mummy brings in the plates,
   and they all sit down.

Mummy has put some meat
   on each of the plates.

One, two, three, four plates.

Soon Mummy brings the pudding.

She cuts the pudding,
   and puts some on each plate.

# The Funny Monkey

One afternoon in school
  Jess reads to Dick and Dora.

She reads the second story
  in the book. It is
  " The Funny Monkey."

Jess will read the story to us.

' One morning Monkey said,
  " I will go out
  and see Rabbit to-day."

Soon he came to Rabbit's home.

" Good morning, Rabbit,"
  said Monkey. " Will you
  come out and play to-day? "

" Yes, yes," said Rabbit,
  " I shall bring some carrots
  for dinner."

When Rabbit was ready
they went to see Nip, the dog.

" Good morning, Nip,"
said Monkey.

" Will you come out and play
to-day ? "

" Yes," said Nip, " I shall bring
some meat and pudding
for dinner."

" First we will play, then
we will eat our dinner,"
said Monkey.

" What will we play ? "
said Rabbit.

" We will run, we will dance,
and then we will do a trick,"
said Monkey. " The best one
will have all the pudding."

" I shall win," said Nip.

" I shall do best," said Rabbit.

" I shall win the pudding,"
said Monkey.

" Now we are all ready
to run," said Rabbit.

They got on a line.
When Monkey said " Go ! "
they all ran.

Rabbit ran best.  He came first,
Nip was second,
and Monkey came third.

Then they had a dance.

Nip said,
   "I can dance like this.
   I can swing up and down,
   and skip in and out."

"See me, see me!" cried Rabbit.
   "I can hop in a ring."

Monkey did a funny dance
   with a plate on his head.

Nip danced the best.

" Now it is time to do a trick.
I will stand on my head,"
said Rabbit.

" See me ! " said Nip.
" I can catch my tail."

" Look, look ! " cried Monkey.
" I can stand on my hands
and hold a carrot in my tail."

Monkey did the best trick.

So they each had some pudding.'

# What is it?

It has a tail.
It can run up a tree.
It will do funny tricks.
   What is it?

It can fly.
It has two feet.
It says, "Quack, quack."
   What is it?

It has four feet.
It has a small tail.
It likes carrots.
It hops.
   What is it?

25

## The Steam Engine

Daddy was going to town,
so Dick and Dora went
to the station with him.

" I want to see the engines,"
said Dick.

They went into the station.

" If you wait here," said Daddy,
" you will see a steam engine."

" Here it comes," cried Dick.
" Here it comes.
How fast it comes
on the lines ! "

Into the station came
the steam engine.
It stopped by Dick and Dora.

They could see two men in it.

" What a big engine ! "
said Dora.

" Yes, and how hot it is ! "
said Dick.  " Look at the fire
in the engine.  It is the fire
that makes the engine go."

A man looked down at them.
" Do you want
to see in the engine ? " he said.

" Oh, yes please," cried Dick
and Dora.

They went up into the engine,
and this is what they saw.

" Now, I will throw some coal
on the fire," said the man.
" I must throw a lot of coal
on the fire to make
the water hot."

" What is that for?" said Dick.

"When the water gets hot
it makes steam," said the man.
"Steam makes the engine go.
Look down by the wheels
and you will see the steam
coming from the engine.

Now it is time for the engine
to take some water."

The engine took a lot of water.

Then the man said,
  " I must look at the wheels."

He jumped down and put
  his hands on the wheels.

First he put his hands
  on the big wheels, and then
  on the small wheels.

Then he went to the wheels
  at the other side of the engine.

" Now we are ready," he said.
  " It is time to go."

"Good-bye," said Dick and Dora.
  " We must see Daddy,
  and say 'Good-bye' to him.
  He is going to town to-day."

# The Little Coal Truck

A little coal truck
was waiting at a station.

The little truck, full of coal,
was waiting for an engine
to pull it up the hill,
and over the hill,
and down the hill
on the other side.

On the other side of the hill
it was cold, and the coal
was wanted for the fires.

Soon a big engine came
puffing into the station.

"Oh, stop, please stop,
big engine!"
cried the little coal truck.

"Please pull me up the hill,
and over the hill,
and down the other side.
They are waiting for my coal."

But the big engine said,
"No, I am busy. I can't,
I'm too busy."

And away it went, saying,
"I'm too busy, much too busy.
I'm too busy, much too busy."

The little coal truck waited
and waited.

Then came a smaller engine,
puffing by.

" Oh, stop, please stop,
small engine ! "
said the little coal truck.

" Please pull me up the hill,
and over the hill,
and down the other side.
They are waiting for my coal."

But the engine went —
puff, puff, puff ! and said,
" I can't, you're too heavy."

And away it went, saying,
" You're too heavy,
much too heavy.
You're too heavy,
much too heavy."

"What shall I do?"
cried the little coal truck.

"On the other side of the hill
it is cold, and they want
my coal."

The little coal truck waited
and waited.

Then a little engine came up —
puff, puff, puff!

"Oh, please stop, little engine!"
said the little coal truck.
"Please pull me up the hill,
and over the hill,
and down the other side.
They are waiting
for my coal."

The little engine looked
at the little coal truck
and stopped.

" You're heavy
  and I'm small,"
  he said.
  " But I think I can.
  Get ready.  Now, catch on."

All the way up the hill
  the little engine was saying,
  " I think I can.
    I think I can.
    I think I can."

At first the engine went fast.

But soon the hill got steep,
  and the little engine
  could not go so fast.  He said,
  " I—think—I—can.
    I—think—I—can.
    I—think—I—can."

35

At last with a big puff —
   " Sh-ss-ss ! " — he came
   to the top of the hill.

Here he could see
   the other side of the hill,
   and away he went,
   going faster and faster, saying,
   " I thought I could.
   I thought I could.
   I thought I could."

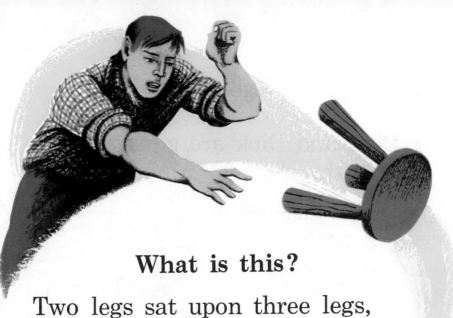

## What is this?

Two legs sat upon three legs,
With one leg on his lap.
In comes four legs,
Runs away with one leg.
Up jumps two legs,
Catches up three legs,
Throws it at four legs.

# Shopping

Dora and Dick are going
   to the shop for Mummy.

Dick must get —
   a pack
   of butter,

   a bag
   of sugar,

and six eggs.

Dora and Dick
   each takes a bag.

Dick will put in his bag
   the butter and the sugar.

Dora will put the eggs
   in her bag.

" Come on, Dora," said Dick.
Then we can see the rabbits
in the pet-shop
on the other side of the road.
" Look," said Dora.
" The pet-shop has white
rabbits."
Dick and Dora wait to see
the white rabbits.

Then they go over to
the other side of the road.

" This is Mr. Brown's shop,
I think," said Dick.  " Yes.
Now let me see what it is
that Mummy wants.

Please, Mr. Brown, may I have —
a pack of butter
a bag of sugar
and six eggs ? "

" Here is the butter,"
said Mr. Brown.
" I will give you a bag
of sugar.  Put the eggs
in your bag, Dora."

One—two—three—
four—five—six eggs.

Dora puts them in her bag.

" I must pay you now,"
said Dick, " for —
a pack of butter,
a bag of sugar
and six eggs."

# Baking Day

" Here you are, Mummy,"
said Dick. "We have
butter, sugar, and eggs.
Now you can make a cake
for us."

" Yes Dick," said Mummy,
" and you and Dora
can help me bake the cake.

Here are the butter and sugar.
Please beat them, Dora.
Dick, will you please beat
the two eggs?"

Dick is beating the eggs
in a dish.

"Look at me," cried Dick,
   "I can beat eggs well.
   Dora, what are you beating
   in your dish?"

"Sugar and butter," she said.

Soon Mummy puts them all
   into her big dish.

Dora stirs it well.

Then Mummy puts it into
   a big cake tin.

"Now it is ready to bake,"
   she said.

"When it has had time to bake
   we will take it out.
   Saturday is Dick's birthday.
   We will eat the cake then."

Dora said, "I think
   I can make a cake now."

## The Birthday Party

" Shall we have a party
for Dick's birthday? "
said Mummy.

"Yes, yes!" cried Dick and Dora.
" We will send letters to Jack
and May, George and Jess."

Dick will send letters
to Jack and George.

Dora will send letters
to Jess and May.

This is what Dick put
in his letters —
" Please come to our party
on Saturday afternoon
at four o'clock."

This is what Dora put
in her letters —
" Please come to our party
on Saturday afternoon
at four o'clock."

Dick reads Dora's letters
to Jess and May.

Dora reads Dick's letters
to George and Jack.

Then they put the letters
in a post box.

Nip went to the post box, too,
to post the letters
for the party.

D

One morning Dora saw
   four letters in the letter-box.

"Two each," cried Dora.

Dick read the letters from
   Jack and George.  Each said
   "Thank you.  I shall come
   to your party, at four o'clock
   on Saturday afternoon."

Dora read the letters from
Jess and May. Each said,
  " Thank you. I shall come
  to your party, at four o'clock
  on Saturday afternoon."

" We will have lots to do,
and will be very busy,"
said Mummy. " Will you help
to get ready for the party?

" Dora can ice the cake
that we made the other day."

" Yes, I will ice the cake,"
said Dora.

" What can I do? " said Dick.

" You can help me to set
the table," said Mummy.

" We will have lots of fun
at the party," said Dick.

" Here they come," cried Dora.

" Here are May, Jess, Jack
and George," cried Dick.
" Let us run to meet them."

" Good afternoon,
good afternoon,"
they all said to each other.

" Good afternoon," said Mummy
to them all.
" Will you have tea now?
It is all ready on the table."

Mummy sat at the top
of the table. On one side
sat Jess, George and Dick.

Dora, Jack and May sat
on the other side.

There was a plate for each.

They all ate some bread
and butter.

" Now I shall cut the cake
and put some on each plate,"
said Mummy.

" This is good cake," said Jack.

" Yes, Dick and Dora helped me
to bake it," said Mummy.

After tea Mummy said,
"Now we will sing."

So they all made a ring,
and they danced and sang,
"Sally go round the moon,
Sally go round the sun,
Sally go round
the chimney pots,
On a Saturday afternoon.
Wh-oo-oop!"

They all sat round the fire
and sang,

"Mother Hen is calling.
  Hark to her call.
Cluck, cluck, cluck,
  I have food for all.

Mother Cow is calling.
  Hark to her call.
Moo, moo, moo,
  I have food for all.

Mother Duck is calling.
  Hark to her call.
Quack, quack, quack,
  I have food for all.

Mother Cat is calling.
  Hark to her call.
Me-ow, me-ow, me-ow,
  I have food for all."

After the singing was over,
   Dick said, " Now for a game.
   Here is a good game.

Stand in two lines.

George, Jess and I will stand
   in one line.

May, Jack and Dora will stand
in the other line."

George's line sang,
" Come, come to see us,
to see us in our house."

May's line sang,
" We will not come to see you,
to see you in your house."

George's line sang,
" Ours is a fine house,
a fine house."

May's line sang,
" If you can pull us,
pull us into your house,
we will see you."

Then they pulled and pulled.

At last George's line pulled
May's line into his house.

# Brown Mouse and
# the Clock

After the game was over,
   Mummy read three stories.
The first was :
" Brown Mouse and the Clock. "

One day Brown Mouse went
   into a field to find some food.

He ran in and out, and as he ran
   he looked all about
   with his two little eyes.

Soon he found a big nut.

He wanted to get hold of it.
   He wanted to take it home,
   but the nut rolled round
   and round and round.

He ran after it,
   but the nut rolled away.
   It rolled by the big tree,
   and he could not find it.

He put his nose to the ground
   to find it.   " Ah, there it is,"
   he said, as he saw the nut
   on the ground.

He ran to get it,
   but the nut rolled and rolled.

Down, down the hill it rolled.

Down, down after it,
   went Mr. Brown Mouse

Down the hill there was a
  little house with a little door.

The nut rolled up to the door,
  and went — tap, tap, tap!

Black Mouse came to the door.

"Good morning, Brown Mouse,"
  he said. "What do you want?"

"I want that nut,"
  said Brown Mouse.

"But it is my nut,"
said Black Mouse.
"It was at my little door."

Mr. Brown Mouse said,
"It is my nut. I found it,
and it rolled down here."

Black Mouse ran with the nut
into the house.

Into the house after him
ran Brown Mouse.

On to the bed
jumped Black Mouse.

On to the bed
jumped Brown Mouse.

Down fell the nut, and rolled
and rolled and rolled.

It rolled into the clock.
Brown Mouse ran in after it.

Then, what
  do you think?

The clock struck One.

Brown Mouse ran.

So fast he ran!

Out of the house
  into the field.

He ran and ran.

He did not stop
  to look for the nut.

He did not like the clock.

Dickory, dickory, dock.
The mouse ran up the clock.
The clock struck One,
The mouse ran down.
Dickory, dickory, dock.

# The Lyre Bird

In Australia
   there is a brown bird.

It has a big tail
   of brown and silver.

It is called a lyre bird.

It can sing very well.

It can make any sound
it hears round about.

It can moo like a cow.
It can meow like a cat.

It can bark like a dog.
It can cluck like a hen.

It can baa like a sheep.
It can quack like a duck.

It can call like a man.
It can cry like a baby.

It can make a sound
like a horse.

It can make the sound
of a saw.

It can sing the songs
of all the other birds
in the forest.

## The Tree House

In Australia
there was a man called Tom.

One Saturday
he went for a walk.

He went out of the town
and over the hill
and into the forest.

He wanted to see a lyre bird.

He walked and walked
and walked.

Then he sat down
in the shadows
and waited.

He waited and waited
but he did not see
a lyre bird.

The sun was very hot.

Tom sat in the shadows
and waited,
but he did not see
a lyre bird.

Soon he got up
and walked on again.

Then he found a very big tree.

It had been cut down
to the ground.

It was a very old tree.

Tom went up to it
and saw that it was hollow.

"This will make a good seat,"
he said.

So he sat on the hollow tree
and waited.

He waited and waited.

Then he saw a brown bird
with a big tail
of brown and silver.

It was a lyre bird,
and it was coming that way.

It ran and jumped
along the ground.

It jumped on to the top
of a little hill
and held its tail high.

" Oh! A lyre bird,"
thought Tom.
" A lyre bird at last!"

Then the bird saw Tom.

It put down its tail
of brown and silver.
It jumped off the little hill
and ran away into the shadows.

" Oh!" thought Tom.
" Now I have lost it."

He jumped down
from the hollow tree
and went home.

The next Saturday
   he went for a walk again.

He went out of the town
   and over the hill
   and into the forest.

This time he took a saw
   with him.

" I will cut a small hole
   in the hollow tree,"
   he thought.

" Then I will sit in the tree
   and look out of the hole.

If the lyre bird comes
   I shall see it,
   but it will not see me
   and it will not run away."

Tom walked and walked.

He came to the hollow tree.

65

He cut a small hole in it
with his saw.

Then he sat in the tree
and waited.

He waited and waited.

Soon the shadows grew long
and the sun began to go down.

Then he saw a brown bird
with a big tail
of brown and silver.

It was the lyre bird,
and it was coming that way.

It ran and jumped
along the ground.

It jumped onto the top
of the little hill.

It held its tail high
and began to sing.

It did not see Tom
   looking out of the hole
   in the hollow tree.

The lyre bird sang.

First of all it made
   the sound of a saw.

Then it barked like a dog,
   and quacked like a duck
   and clucked like a hen.

Then it called like a man
   and cried like a baby.

Then it sang the songs
of all the other birds
in the forest.

Tom was very happy.

" What a good place
this hollow tree is,"
he said.

" I can see the lyre bird
but the lyre bird
cannot see me."

Then at last
he went out of the tree
and walked home.

After a time
Tom made the hollow tree
into a little house.

He made a door
and some windows.

He put in a small table
and a seat and a bed.

" This is a very good house,"
he thought.
" Here I can see the lyre bird
but the lyre bird
cannot see me."

This is a true story,
and Tom's tree house
is in Australia to this day.

# The Tar Baby

Mr. Fox had a fine garden.
In it were fine carrots
and turnips.

Each morning, Mr. Fox
went to his garden
to get carrots and turnips
for his dinner.

Each morning he saw
that some one had eaten
some of his fine carrots.

" I must find out
who is taking my carrots,"
thought Mr. Fox.
" I must catch the one
who has been in my garden.
I will hide at the side
of the garden."

So Mr. Fox hid at the side
of his garden. Along came
White Tail, the rabbit.
He hopped over to the carrots
and ate six of them.
Then off he went.

"I must stop this," said Mr. Fox.
"I shall make a tar baby."

Mr. Fox made a tar baby
with sticks and black tar.

Then he laughed and said,
" I'll play a trick
on White Tail.
I shall stand the tar baby up
in the garden. Then I'll hide
to see what he will do."

Along came White Tail.
  He looked at the tar baby
  and said, "Good morning."

But the tar baby did not talk.

"Good morning,"
  said White Tail again.
  "Do you like
  Mr. Fox's carrots?"

But the tar baby did not talk.

"You are stuck up,"
  said White Tail.
  "I will make you talk.
  I will hit you."

So he hit
  the tar baby
  with his hand.
  It stuck fast
  to the sticky
  black tar.

He pulled and pulled,
but he could not get
his hand away.

Mr. Fox was at the side
of the garden. He laughed,
but was very still.

"Let me go," cried White Tail,
"or I will hit you
with my other hand."

But the tar baby did not talk
and did not let him go.

So White Tail hit the tar baby
with the other hand,
and that stuck fast, too.

Mr. Fox laughed again,
but was very still.

"Let me go, or I will kick you,"
cried White Tail.

But the tar baby did not talk
and did not let him go.

White Tail gave the tar baby
a kick with one foot.
But his foot stuck fast.

He pulled and pulled,
but could not pull his foot
away from the tar.

"Let me go, let me go,"
called White Tail,
"or I will kick you
with the other foot."

The tar baby did not talk
and did not let him go.

Mr. Fox laughed again.

White Tail kicked the tar baby
with the other foot,
and that stuck fast, too.

"Let me go, let me go,"
called White Tail,
"or I'll hit you with my head."

Then he hit the tar baby
with his head,
and that stuck fast, too.

Mr. Fox came up to White Tail.
"How stuck up you are!"
he said.

And he laughed and laughed
and laughed at White Tail
stuck fast to the tar baby.

"Please, please let me go.
I won't eat your carrots
again," cried White Tail.

"I will put you in a pot
of hot water," said Mr. Fox.

F

"Oh yes," said White Tail,
"make it as hot as you like.
But please don't throw me
in the briars."

"I'll throw you in the river."
said Mr. Fox.

"Do that if you like,"
said White Tail, "but please
don't throw me in the briars."

"I'll give you to Mr. Wolf,"
said Mr. Fox.

"Do that," said White Tail.
"I'll make a good dinner
for Mr. Wolf, but please
don't throw me in the briars."

"So you don't like the briars?"
said Mr. Fox. "Well, well!
I am going to throw you
in the briars."

He took White Tail by the leg
and threw him
with the tar baby
into the briars.

The briars helped White Tail
to get off the sticky black tar.

Away he ran up the hill.

"I like briars.
Good-bye, Mr. Fox.
You won't catch me again."

# Fire! Fire!

One day Dick and Daddy
   were walking along the road.
   They had been to see a game
   of football.

" Look, look, Daddy!
   There is a house on fire.
   Can you see the fire
   near the chimney ? "

" Yes, we must find a phone box,"
   said Daddy, " and send a call
   to the fire station."

" Look, over there,"
   cried Dick.
   " On the other side
   of the road there
   is a phone box."

Dick and Daddy ran over.

Daddy opened the glass door
of the phone box.

He picked up the phone
and rang 999.

" Fire station, please," he said.

" There is a house on fire
in George Road,"
he said to the fireman.

" We will wait by this box.
The fire is near here."

Dick and Daddy waited
at the phone box.

Soon the big fire engine
was coming up the hill.
It came up very fast.

The firemen jumped out.

" The fire is in that house
over there," cried Dick.

" Out with the hose,"
said one fireman.
" Bring it along here.
We must send some water
to the top of the house.
Send it around the chimney."

One fireman hit on the door.
All was very still.
He hit again and again.

" No one home," he said.
Then he stopped,
and looked up.

" Me-ow, me-ow ! "

Up there was a little kitten.

" Me-ow, me-ow, get me down,"
said Kitty.

" Out with the ladder,"
said the fireman. " It must be
very hot up there
for that kitten."

Up, up went the ladder
    to the top of the house.

Up, up went the fireman
    to the top of the ladder.

" Me-ow, me-ow ! " said Kitty.

Soon the fireman had Kitty
    in his hands. He came down
    to the ground.

Kitty was very pleased
to be away from the hot fire.

The water put the fire out
very soon.

The ladder was taken down.
The hose was put round
and round on the engine.

Then the fireman said to Dick,
"You are a very good boy
to tell us about the fire,
and to wait for us
by the phone box.

"Would you like to ride
with us to the fire station?"

"Oh yes, please," said Dick.

So Dick and Daddy had a ride
on the big fire-engine
up the road and around
to the fire station.

"Now," said the fireman,
  "I will take you around
  the fire station.

There are three fire-engines.
  See, each engine has ladders
  and rolls of hose.

Here are our hats."

The fireman put a hat
  on Dick's head.

"I think I will be a fireman
  when I grow up,"
  said Dick.

"Good-bye," said Daddy.

"Good-bye," said Dick,
  "and thank you very much."

# A Game

## Two Little Dickie Birds

Two little dickie birds,
Sitting on a wall.
One named Peter,
One named Paul.
Fly away, Peter.
Fly away, Paul.
Come back, Peter.
Come back, Paul.

Can you play the game of two little dickie birds?

Get two small pieces of paper.

Write, on one piece of paper, the name of the first birdie, like this:

Peter

Write, on the other piece of paper, the name of the second birdie, like this:

Paul

Stick the piece of paper with Peter on it on to the *first* finger of your *right* hand.

Stick the piece of paper with Paul on it on to the *first* finger of your *left* hand.

Then ask your teacher what you must do to play the game of two little dickie birds.

# Puzzles

I am red.
I use coal.
I use wood.
I make things hot.
    What am I ?

I have a face.
I have two hands
I am round.
I show the time.
    What am I ?

I am round.
I grow on a tree.
My skin is red.
I am white inside.
    What am I ?

I wear a tin hat.
I wear a uniform.
I run up ladders.
I ride on an engine.
    Who am I ?

I can go up hills.
I go very fast.
Steam makes me go.
I run on lines.
    What am I ?

I am black.
I have ink inside me.
I am used for writing.
    What am I ?

I grow on a tree.
I grow in hot lands.
I have milk inside
    me.
I am white inside.
I am hairy outside.
    What am I ?

I have a funny face.
I wear funny clothes.
I play in a circus.
I jump and run about.
    Who am I ?

# Word List

This list contains the 219 new words used in Book 3. Words marked with an asterisk are derivatives—verb variants (ending -s, -es, -ed, -ing), simple plurals of known singular nouns and vice versa, simple apostrophes, and words ending in -(e)n and -(e)r where the stem is already known.

1 * going
school
bag

2 met
Jess
* takes

3 * seats
book
* Jack's
reads

4 * read
story
each
first

5 cannot
wolf
catch
road
man
straw

6 give
want

7 took
gave
made
second
sticks

8 third
bricks
your

9 * pig's
tapped
door
hair
chin

10 * I'll
huff
puff
blow
* huffed
* puffed

blew
ate

11 could

12 o'clock
turnips
ready
apple
* apples

13 coming

14 fair
town
hill
barrel

16 top

17 chimney
eat
pot
hot

89

water
lid

18 dinner
time
set
table
our

19 * brings
plates
meat
pudding
* cuts
* puts
* plate

20 afternoon
to-day
carrots

21 trick
best

22 win

23 head
* danced

24 stand
tail
* hands
* carrot

25 feet
* says
quack
* likes

26 steam
engine
station
wait

27 * comes
* lines
stopped
men
fire
* looked

28 coal
lot

29 * gets
* makes
wheels

30 other
side

31 truck
* waiting
full
pull
over
cold
* wanted

* fires
* puffing

32 busy
* can't
* I'm
* saying
much

33 * waited
* smaller
* you're
heavy

35 think
steep

36 last
* faster
thought

37 * legs
sat
upon
lap
* catches

38 shopping
pack
butter
sugar
taking

39 * pet-shop

Mr.
Brown's
* wants
* brown

40 pay

41 baking
cake
help
* bake

42 beat
* beating
dish

43 stirs
tin
Saturday
birthday

44 party
send
letters
George

45 post
box

46 * letter-box
thank

47 very
ice
* lots

48 * meet

49 there
bread
* helped

50 sang
Sally
round
moon
sun
* pots
* after

51 calling
hark
* call
cluck
food
cow
moo
me-ow

52 * singing
game

53 * George's
* May's
* ours
find
* pulled

54 mouse
* clock

stories
field
about
* eyes

55 found
nut
rolled
ground

56 * tap
black

58 struck
dickory
dock

59 lyre
bird
Australia
silver
* called

60 sound
hears
bark
baa
sheep
baby
songs
* birds
* trees

61 Tom

|  | forest | 70 | tar |  | river |
|---|---|---|---|---|---|
| 62 | * walked<br>again<br>had<br>been | | fox<br>garden<br>were<br>* eaten<br>who | 80 | * walking<br>football<br>near<br>phone |
| 63 | old<br>hollow<br>along<br>held | | * taking<br>hide | 81 | opened<br>glass<br>picked<br>rang<br>firemen |
| 64 | lost | 71 | hid<br>* hopped | | |
| 65 | next<br>hole | 72 | laughed | 82 | hose<br>fireman<br>around |
| 66 | grew<br>began | 73 | talk<br>* fox's<br>stuck<br>sticky | 83 | Kitty<br>ladder |
| 67 | * barked<br>* quacked<br>* clucked | 74 | still<br>or<br>kick | 85 | * pleased<br>* taken<br>tell<br>boy<br>would |
| 68 | happy<br>place<br>windows | 75 | foot | | |
| | | 76 | * kicked | 86 | * ladders |
| 69 | true<br>Tom's | 77 | won't | | * rolls<br>* hats<br>grow |
| | | 78 | * don't<br>briars | | |